Stilts,
Somersaults,
and
Headstands

Stilts, Somersaults, and Headstands

Game Poems Based on a Painting
by PETER BREUGHEL

Kathleen Fraser

Atheneum   New York   1968

For my first born, David Ian
his father, Jack
his grandparents, Ian and Marjorie
Who have kept me singing and laughing

Copyright © 1968 by Kathleen Fraser
All rights reserved
Library of Congress catalog card number 68-12236
Published simultaneously in Canada by
McClelland and Stewart Ltd.
Manufactured in the United States of America
Printed by Reehl Litho, Inc., New York
Bound by H. Wolff, New York
Designed by David Rogers
First Edition

Contents

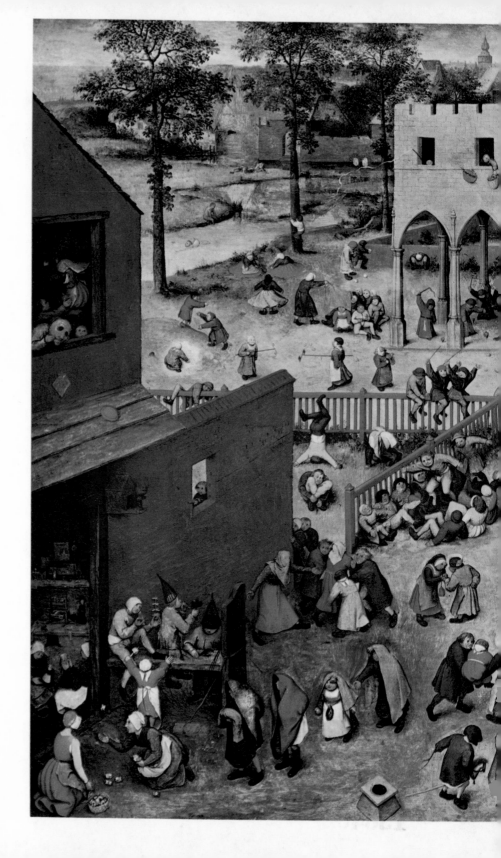

Nᴏᴛ ᴛᴏᴏ ʟᴏɴɢ ᴀɢᴏ I saw for the first time the very painting you are seeing in this book. It was an exciting moment. There before me was a picture, called *Children's Games,* painted in 1560—over four hundred years ago—by a Dutchman named Pieter Breughel. Yet as old as it was, the painting showed children playing many of the games I had played in my own childhood! When I recognized boys playing King of the Mountain and Balancing a Broom and girls playing Jacks and Dolls, I was filled with so many happy memories, that I decided to write a book of play poems and chants especially to go with the games in this painting. Maybe you'll discover many games you already know how to play, and maybe some new ones, too.

Kathleen Fraser

HOOPS

BALLOON

TUG OF WAR

SHOUTING INTO A BARREL

RIDING A BARREL

Hoops

What is a hoop?
A hoop is a loop.
A loop-de-loop circle
of rubber or metal.
A metal hoop wobbles
on sidewalks and cobbles.
The cobblestones sing
with the ring of a hoop.
A hoop is for chasing
and windy-day racing.
You run down the hill
'til the hoop stands still.

Balloon

Dear little balloon,
my tiny piece of color,
I will eat a big breakfast
and blow you full of wind.
I will tie you with a string
and float you near the sun.
I will show you where
the butterflies go swimming.

Tug of War

No one is quite sure
how to win at Tug of War
except that you pull
and pullll   and pulllllll
and just as you're sure
you are winning,
the other team pulls
and pulllls   and pulllllllls
and you fall their way
and then they fall your way
but
if everyone on your team
should suddenly take a big breath
and tug all together
with arms around each other
then you might just possibly win.

Shouting into a Barrel

Barrels are very rare
and hard to come by
so
if you ever see a barrel
in the street,
be sure to shout into it.
You can shout hellllloooooo
or good-bye
or
I'd like to push Henry
into a big pile of mud.

Riding a Barrel

Riding a barrel is harder
than shouting into one.
It is curved
but you are straight.
When it begins to roll,
you begin to fall.

But if you learn to keep
your balance on a barrel,
a circus may come by that day
and let you ride
on its elephant.

KNOCKING OVER CASTLES MADE WITH MARBLES

CATCH THE WOODEN FISH

TIP—CAT

Knocking Over Castles Made With Marbles

See these little piles of marbles.
They are my castles.
And you are the soldiers,
come to knock them down.
With your pockets full of rocks,
you've come to wreck my dream
while I sit in the dust
and cry and cry and cry.

Catch the Wooden Fish

Catch the wooden fish,
and put it into a dish.
Squeeze on plenty of lemon,
then pop it into the oven.

When the wood is tender,
flavor with coriander.
Tie it with paper and string
and present to a wooden king.

He'll probably give you a medal
and invite you to sit at his table.
Twixt he and his wooden queen
and three dishes of wooden ice-cream.

Tip—Cat

With our sticks,
we will be like swordsmen,
but not really.

We'll dip and lunge
and plunge at each other's hearts,
but not really.

We'll rip our shirts
and try to trip each other,
but not really.

We'll make the most terrible sounds
and pretend we are done for,
but not really.

FOLLOW THE LEADER

WRESTLING

MARBLES

PARADE

Follow the Leader

Whatever he does, you have to do too,
because he is the leader.
When he jumps off the porch, you have to jump too
(even when you're a little bit scared),
because he is the leader.
If he yells "blueberry" very loud
or says "Hello" to a frog,
you have to do all those things
because he is the leader.

But then his turn is over.
And you are next.
And everyone stands behind you
and waits for you to begin
and they have to do whatever silly things
you can think of
because YOU are the leader now.

Wrestling

I like wrestling with Herbie because
he's my best friend.
We poke each other
(but not very hard)
and punch each other
(but not very hard)
and roll on the grass
and pretend to have fights
just to make our sisters scream.
But sometimes if he hits me too much
and it hurts,
I get mad
and I punch him back
as hard as I can
and then we both are crying
and going into our houses
and slamming our back doors on each other.
But the next day, if it's sunny,
we come out into our yards
and grin at each other,
and sometimes he gives me an apple
or I give him a cookie and
then we start wrestling again.

Marbles

Immies.
Purees.
Agates.
Shooters.
In a circle.
In a row.
Immies.
Purees.
Agates.
Shooters.
Knock one out
or down a hole.
Immies.
Purees.
Agates.
Shooters.
If I win,
I keep them all.

Parade

A parade! A parade!
Let's have a parade!
To celebrate snow
and mud puddles and jade.

The girls can wear costumes
and lipstick and pearls.
The boys can make speeches
and wave to the world.

We'll carry big signs
and march to the zoo
and throw free cookies
to the sad kangaroo.

A parade! A parade!
Let's have a parade!
To celebrate snow
and mud puddles and jade.

STILTS

SWINGING ON A RAIL

BROOM BALANCING

Stilts

Little stilts are for learning to keep your balance on
    and
Big stilts are for looking in a friend's window when he's eating lunch
    and
Little stilts are for saying "I'm taller than you are"
    and
Big stilts are for counting the eggs in a cuckoo's nest
    and
Little stilts are for rubbing noses with a pony
    and
Big stilts are for pretending your head is a white cloud.

Swinging on a Rail

Have you ever seen a rail
that didn't need someone
to swing on it?
Someone to hang by his knees from it,
or to turn in circles over it?
Someone
to look upside down at it,
with his long legs criss-crossing it?
Someone
to dangle his toes from it
while he's daydreaming under it?

Broom Balancing

Millicent can play the flute
and Francine can dance a jig,
but I can balance a broom.

Susanna knows how to bake cookies
and Harold can stand on one foot
but I can balance a broom.

Jeffry can climb a ladder backwards
and Andrew can count to five thousand and two,
but I can balance a broom.

Do you think a circus might discover me?

HOBBYHORSE

FIFE AND DRUM

MUD PIE

WHICH HAND?

Hobbyhorse

Some horses run in the field
and others are fastened tight
to rockers,
but a hobbyhorse can go anywhere
you go.
Store horses are painted
so you have to be careful,
but you can make a hobbyhorse
from a tree branch
or an old broom handle.
You can tell a hobbyhorse
your secrets.
You can ride him to the moon.

Fife and Drum

Fife and drum,
fife and drum,
down the winding
street we come.

Stick on drum,
mouth on fife,
people running
for their life.

Here we come,
fife and drum.
Where's the candy?
Throw us some!

Mud Pie

The recipe for mud pie
is one cup of water
and enough dirt to make mud.
You stir it around in a broken pot
and pour it into a pie tin
or whatever old pan
your mother will give you.
Back yards are best for
baking mud pies in.
The sun beats down
and gets hot like an oven.
And pretty soon your pie is done.
But don't eat it!
Give it to a beetle.

Which Hand?

Has he got it in his left hand?
Has he got it in his right hand?

Is it under his thumb
or curled inside his fingers?

Is one hand pretending
that the other really has it?

Is the other full of treasures
that it never wants to part with?

Oh right hand, oh left hand,
please give away your secret!

WHO AM I GOING TO CHOOSE?

TURN YOURSELF AROUND

TREE CLIMBING

WATERWINGS

PIGGYBACK

KING OF THE MOUNTAIN

FLYING A RIBBON

Who Am I Going to Choose?

Who am I going to choose?
Someone with polka-dot shoes.
Who am I going to pick?
A boy with his hat on a stick.
Where are we going to go?
To the caves of the Rummy-tum-toe.
Why are we going there?
To straighten the curls in our hair.
What are we going to eat?
Some fudge and some pickled pigs' feet.
When are we coming back?
As soon as the ocean goes smack.

Turn Yourself Around

Red skirts, red skirts
a'whirling, a'whirling.
White skirts, white skirts
a'twirling, a'twirling.

Turn yourself around
on the tips of your toes.
Turn yourself around
and out your skirt goes.

Red skirts in the sunshine,
white skirts in the moonshine,
floating like dragonflies
dancing on the wind.

Tree Climbing

This is my tree,
my place to be alone in,
my branches for climbing,
my green leaves for hiding in,
my sunshine for reading,
my clouds for dreaming,
my sky for singing,
my tree, my beautiful tree.

Waterwings

Is that an angel
in the water?
Or a trout sprouting wings?
No, it's Annie's little brother
learning how to swim.
He's scared to dunk his head
so he wears his waterwings
and pretends that he's a little boat
floating among the fishes.

Piggyback

I wish my friend were a kangaroo.
Then I could jump into his pocket
and go bumping around.
But he's not.
He's a boy.
So we play piggyback and I put my hands
around his neck and he carries me
on his back because
he's bigger and I'm littler.
But when we're done,
then my other friend put his hands
around my neck because
I'm bigger and he's littler.

King of the Mountain

"I am the King,
and this is my mountain,"
said Melvin.

"I am the King,
and you have to do what I say,"
said Melvin.

"I am the King,
and you can't come on my property,"
said Melvin.

Then Michael ran to the top
of the hill where Melvin
was making his speech
and pushed him down . . .

"I am the King,
and this is my mountain,"
said Michael.

Flying a Ribbon

What is your favorite mystery?
    It's the wind.
Where does the wind go?
    It goes where it wants to go.
Can you hear it?
    Only if it's in a hurry.
    When the wind is quiet,
    it runs through the street
    in sneakers.
How do you know the wind's secret?
    I tie a long white ribbon
    to the end of a stick
    and when the wind comes by
    it makes the ribbon fly
    in its direction.

JACKS

RATTLE

DOLLS

BLOWING BUBBLES

BLINDMAN'S BUFF

PLAYING WITH A PET BIRD

MAKE—BELIEVE CHRISTENING

Jacks

Jacks look like stars
and the ball you throw to catch them
like a small red moon.
While the moon's bouncing back
your hand must be quick
to collect star after star.
The rules say
if you touch too much
or let the moon roll away
you lose the game.

Rattle

Grab tight to its handle
and shake . . . knock, knock
                clack, clack.
The rattle lets someone know
you are there.
If he laughs, you have made a friend.
If he says "Go away,"
you know he's the quiet sort
and you find another friend.
With a rattle you can wake the world up!

Dolls

Dolls are like people.
When they are new and shiny
it is easy to look at them
but hard to play with at first.
Each day you play a little longer
and then your new doll
becomes Sandy or Lulu
or Marmalade May
and when you go visiting
a friend with a doll
you know yours is the one
you like holding.

Blowing Bubbles

Bubbles are big enough
to see your face in
or a real rainbow
and small enough to get lost
almost as fast as they arrive.
How sad . . .
But look! Here comes a new one.

Blindman's Buff

With a scarf around his eyes,
how can the blindman catch us?
With no way to see it,
how strange the world must seem.

The blindman reaches out
with all ten fingers.
He must find us and touch us
and guess our hidden names.

First he'll feel long, silky hair
and guess that it is Ellen.
Then he'll touch thick, glossy braids
and know Rebecca Jane.

And when he feels a funny hat
and recognizes Christopher,
we'll dance around the blindman
and let him see again.

Playing With a Pet Bird

Little bird, your leg is hurt.
Have you fallen from the nest?
Did your mother fly away?
I will take care of you,
little bird.
You can sit on my table
and drink my milk.

Make—Believe Christening

Mama (a girl) wears a new hat
and Daddy (the biggest boy)
walks first, holding the baby
(which has to be a doll
or your littlest friend) . . .
Then come the aunts and
uncles and cousins bringing
money for the church
and someone says a prayer
and tells the baby to be good.
Then everyone sings a song
and goes back to the porch
for a glass of grape juice
or a glass of milk.

MAKE—BELIEVE WEDDING PROCESSION

RUNNING THE GAUNTLET

RIDING A FENCE

SOMERSAULTS & HEADSTANDS

Make—Believe Wedding Procession

First you choose a husband
and a wife and then
you find someone to be the holy man
(who knows all the right words to say).
There are lots of flowers
and you stand under a tree and say
I do and I will and I promise . . .
Then a kiss on the hand
and a big parade through everybody's yard
with roses in the hair of the girls
and flags in the hands of the boys.

BIG NEIGHBORHOOD BOY:
> Want to run the gauntlet?

NEW LITTLE BOY:
> How do you play?

BIG NEIGHBORHOOD BOY:
> Well, *we* all sit in a row on the grass, across from each other, and *you* have to run through our feet from one end of the row to the other.

NEW LITTLE BOY:
> Through all your knees and all your boots?

BIG NEIGHBORHOOD BOY:
> Yep.

NEW LITTLE BOY:
> Will you kick and bump? Will you trip me?

BIG NEIGHBORHOOD BOY:
> Well, sort of . . .

NEW LITTLE BOY:
> Will it hurt?

BIG NEIGHBORHOOD BOY:
> Not if you cross your eyes and wiggle your ears and run as fast as a lizard.

NEW LITTLE BOY:
> I think I'll just watch for a while.

Riding a Fence

Where do you go when
you ride on a fence?
I go hither and thither
and whither and hence.

If the fence is my stallion,
I trot through the grass
and fed him sweet carrots
and green sassafrass.

If the fence is my tiger,
we roar through the trees
and chase after burglars
and robbers and thieves.

If the fence is my camel,
I straddle his humps
and we head for the desert
with delicate bumps.

If the fence is my dolphin,
we swim in the ocean
and send secret codes
to the King of the Salmon.

What are you doing?
> I'm turning a somersault.

How do you do it?
> I put my head in the grass
> and roll over like a snail.

Could you turn a wintersault?
> No, because my head would
> get cold in the snow.

Now, what are you doing?
> A headstand.

Is it like a somersault?
> Well, sort of, but you stop
> in the middle.

How do you keep from falling?
> I pretend everyone else
> is walking upside down.